Things in My House

By Joe Kaufman

GOLDEN PRESS
Western Publishing Company, Inc.
Racine, Wisconsin

Copyright © 1968, 1963 by
Western Publishing Company, Inc.
All rights reserved. Produced in U.S.A.

Seventh Printing, 1976

GOLDEN, A LITTLE GOLDEN BOOK®, and GOLDEN PRESS®
are trademarks of Western Publishing Company, Inc. No part of this
book may be reproduced or copied in any form without written per-
mission from the publisher.

There are all kinds
of things in my house:

a hammer,

a shoe,

a pencil,

a sock,

an apple,

a flower,

a fork,

and a clock.

A saw,

a leaf,

a ball,

a bat,

an umbrella,

glasses,

a block,

and a hat.

A kettle,

a lemon,

a glove,

a toy boat,

a toothbrush,

a ruler,

| 1 | 2 | 3 | 4 | 5 | 6 |

a horn,

and  a coat.

A candle,

a doll,

a cookie,

a nail,

a locomotive,

an onion,

a shovel, and a pail.

A fireman's hat,

a walnut,

a lamp,

scissors,

a cup,

a brush,

and a stamp.

An airplane,

a puppet,

an orange,

a spoon,

a window,

and outside...
stars and the moon.